Key Stage
Developing Literacy

WORD LEVEL

SPELLING ACTIVITIES FOR LITERACY LESSONS

year
9

Ray Barker and Christine Moorcroft

A & C BLACK

Contents

Published 2003 by A & C Black Publishers Limited
37 Soho Square, London W1D 3QZ
www.acblack.com

ISBN 0-7136-6482-7

Copyright text © Ray Barker and Christine Moorcroft, 2003
Copyright illustrations © Brett Hudson, 2003
Copyright cover illustration © Paul Cemmick, 2003
Editor: Lucy Poddington

The authors and publishers would like to thank Claire Truman for her advice in producing this series of books.

Printed in Great Britain by St Edmundsbury Press Ltd, Bury St Edmunds, Suffolk.

A & C Black uses paper produced with elemental chlorine-free pulp, harvested from managed sustainable forests.

Introduction

Key Stage 3 Developing Literacy: Word Level is a series of photocopiable resources for Years 7, 8 and 9, designed to be used during English lessons or in other subjects across the curriculum to help with the spelling of key terms and new words. They are also ideal for homework. The books focus on the Word level strand of the Key Stage 3 National Strategy *Framework for teaching English: Years 7, 8 and 9*.

Each book supports the teaching of English by providing a series of activities that develop essential literacy spelling skills. Literacy, of course, includes more than these basic skills, but language is about communication, and the ability to spell words accurately is essential in creating meaning. Writers need to develop spelling strategies which they can use with confidence – leaving them free to concentrate on developing, arranging and constructing ideas.

Spelling in English is not easy because English includes words and language conventions from many languages and cultures. However, English spelling is not as irregular as it may appear: many of the exceptions to the rules share spelling patterns with other words, and can be linked to a common root word or language. **Word Level Year 9** provides revision and consolidation of spelling rules and exceptions, but also encourages pupils to develop skills and strategies which are progressive and transferable. These include:

- splitting words into syllables;
- being aware of phonemes and the variety of ways in which they can be spelled;
- finding words within words;
- using mnemonics to help memorisation;
- investigating the derivation of root words, prefixes and suffixes;
- using the Look, Say, Cover, Write and Check strategy.

How to use this book

Each double-page activity in this book is based around a Year 9 Word level objective. The left-hand page is a **starter** activity, which may be an OHT for use with the whole class, or an activity for the pupils to work on in pairs or small groups. The right-hand page provides a **consolidation** activity to reinforce the main teaching objective, followed by an **extension** activity (**Now try this!**) to reinforce and develop the pupils' learning.

Starter activities

Each starter activity is designed to be used as a short introduction to the consolidation activity that follows it. Evidence has shown that lessons which start with a sharp focus on a specific objective – for only ten to fifteen minutes – grab the pupils' attention and ensure that the whole class is clear about what to do and about the expected outcome of the lesson. The starter activities in this book address the objectives in a direct and explicit way. They involve both reading and writing, and encourage fast-paced learning and interaction. A range of teaching and learning styles are used – from independent to teacher supported – focusing on the following key teacher interactions:

- direction
- modelling
- explanation
- exploration
- discussion
- demonstration
- scaffolding
- questioning
- investigation
- reflection and evaluation.

The starter activities in this book also provide valuable opportunities to revise previous learning. New terms are introduced and other important terms are revised during the starter activity; these are highlighted by being boxed or set in bold type. All the highlighted terms are explained in the glossary on page 64, which can be photocopied for the pupils to file and use for reference.

The starter activities can be photocopied and used in the following ways:

- as an OHT for whole-class teaching, with pupils giving answers orally or coming to the front to help complete the sheet;
- as a group activity, with each group working through the sheet or with different groups focusing on different parts of the sheet;
- as a timed activity, with the pupils completing as much of the sheet as possible within a time limit;
- in conjunction with appropriate class texts to help illustrate a principle;
- as preparatory work for an investigation, to be carried out for homework;
- as a stand-alone revision sheet for groups or individuals;
- as a tool for assessment.

Consolidation activities

The *Framework for teaching English: Years 7, 8 and 9* advocates that lessons should continue with a development of the main teaching points. The consolidation activities in this book can be used as the focus of this development, freeing teachers to work intensively with groups or individuals on the current objective.

The instructions in the activities are presented clearly to enable pupils to work independently. There are also opportunities for the pupils to work in pairs or groups, to encourage discussion and co-operation. A dictionary icon reminds pupils of the importance of checking their answers in a dictionary. Hints and reminders are given in boxes at the page margin.

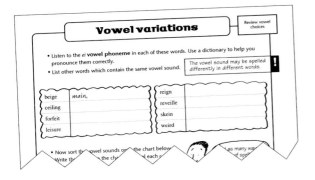

Encourage pupils to compile individual spelling logs by listing words they frequently misspell, identifying the problem areas of each word and writing down strategies to help them remember how to spell it. They should regularly review their progress by ticking off the words which no longer cause problems and by highlighting those that need further attention. Encourage the pupils to refer to their spelling logs as they write.

Extension activities

Each page ends with a **Now try this!** extension activity. These more challenging activities may be appropriate for only some of the pupils; it is not expected that the whole class should complete them. The pupils may need to record their answers in a notebook or on a separate piece of paper.

Organisation

The pupils will need access to a range of dictionaries (including etymological ones) and thesauruses. ICT facilities will also be useful for research into word derivations. Spell-checkers can be valuable but the pupils need to be aware that they cannot be used in examinations and that they do not check for homophones. The pupils should also remember that some spell-checkers use American spelling and grammar (this can be a useful teaching point for the differences between English and American English).

All the activities in this book are linked closely to the requirements of the *Framework for teaching English,* but it is not intended that they should be presented in any specific order, unless stated. This resource is versatile and is intended for teachers to use according to the literacy needs of their pupils.

Some of the activities can be linked with work in other subjects; however, it is envisaged that most of the activities will be carried out during English lessons.

Teachers' notes

The notes provided at the foot of the activity pages contain additional instructions for using the sheets. These can be masked before photocopying. The notes on pages 6–9 offer further practical advice on making the most of the activity sheets, including extra teaching ideas, suggestions for applying the work to texts the pupils are studying, and answers to selected activities.

Teachers' notes

The notes below expand upon those provided at the foot of each activity page. They give ideas for making the most of the activity sheets, including suggestions for introducing the teaching objectives and for follow-up work based on the sheet.

Spelling

Consonant conundrums (pages 10–11). This activity looks at hard and soft consonant sounds, focusing on c, g, gh and ph. The **starter** activity gives the pupils practice in identifying the hard and soft sounds of letters in particular words, which leads on to formulating strategies to help them spell the words. Soft c and g sounds are often followed by an e, i or y; hard c and g sounds are often followed by a, o or u (or consonants). This helps to show why words such as *knowledgeable* and *traceable* retain the e before the suffix *-able*. The **consolidation** activity looks at the different ways in which the gh letter combination is pronounced. When gh is at the beginning of a word, it makes a hard g sound; in the middle or at the end of a word, gh can make an f sound or be part of the vowel sound.

Vowel variations (pages 12–13). This activity focuses on the spelling and pronunciation of vowel phonemes. The **starter** activity provides an opportunity to practise using dictionaries to help with the pronunciation of words. The **consolidation** activity shows the variety of sounds created by the ei letter combination. The rule 'i before e except after c, whenever it rhymes with me' can be used, but there are many exceptions. The **extension** activity (**Now try this!**) reminds the pupils that the addition of just one letter to a word can change both the vowel sound and the meaning.

Coming to a sticky end (pages 14–15). In this activity the pupils revise rules concerning suffixes. The **starter** activity looks at words ending in *-ible* and *-able*: complete root words are more likely to take the suffix *-able* and incomplete roots tend to take *-ible*. However, there are many exceptions to the rule. As a follow-up, the pupils could develop strategies such as mnemonics to help them spell the words which are exceptions. The **consolidation** and **extension** activities look at a variety of suffixes and their impact on the spelling of the root words. The addition of the suffix *-y* does not normally change the spelling of a root word unless it ends in e (for example, *grease – greasy*), but exceptions include *hole – holey* (to avoid confusion with *holy*) and *winter – wintry*. The addition of *-ly* usually only changes the spelling of root words ending in *-y* (for example, *cheeky – cheekily*) or e (for example, *true – truly, miserable – miserably*).

Plural posers (pages 16–17). This activity looks at plurals of nouns ending in f, fe, o and y. In the **starter** activity, the pupils will find that most words ending in f or fe change to *-ves* in the plural (for example, *wife – wives; thief – thieves*). Exceptions include *roofs* and words ending in ff, such as *cliffs*. Words ending in a consonant plus y change the y to *-ies* (for example, *baby – babies*). Words ending in a vowel plus y simply add an s (for example, *monkey – monkeys*). In the **consolidation** activity, the pupils investigate further examples and revise the rules for words ending in o. Many take *-es* (for example, *volcano – volcanoes*). Words that take only s tend to be foreign words, shortened forms or words with a vowel preceding the o (for example, *piano – pianos; ratio – ratios*). The **extension** activity looks at irregular plurals and their derivation. During the **plenary** session, draw out the rules for forming plurals and explain that not all plurals follow the rules because many English words are derived from other languages.

A blast from the past (pages 18–19). This activity helps the pupils to realise that English is an evolving language and that the peculiarities of our spelling system arise from this. In the **starter** activity, the pupils read a piece of text from the fifteenth century, with original spelling. Spelling patterns can be observed: for example, y was used instead of i in many words, and double vowels were seldom used. The **consolidation** activity develops the work using a passage by Chaucer, which describes a slapstick chase of a fox that has stolen a cockerel. The pupils could research the meanings of words no longer used today, using the Internet or a dictionary such as *The Cambridge Encyclopedia of the English Language* (David Crystal, Cambridge University Press). As a follow-up, ask the pupils to investigate language in class texts from other periods in a similar way.

First things first (pages 20–21). This activity reinforces the meanings of prefixes and their impact on the spelling of root words. The answers to the **starter** activity are: **under-** 1. *underdone* 2. *underpaid* 3. *undertake* 4. *understand*

5. *underhand* 6. *undergrowth*; **ex-** 1. *expel* 2. *expand* 3. *exhale* 4. *execute* 5. *exclaim* 6. *excavate* 7. *extinguish* 8. *exile* 9. *extend* 10. *experiment*; **sur-** 1. *surveyor* 2. *surplus* 3. *survivor* 4. *surrender* 5. *surface*. The **consolidation** activity gives a range of different prefixes to research and provides an opportunity to develop dictionary skills. The **extension** activity highlights that the addition of a prefix does not change the spelling of the root word; this is especially relevant to commonly misspelled words such as *disappear, disapprove, irrelevant* and *misspell*.

Put an end to it! (pages 22–23).

The addition of a suffix often changes the spelling of the root word; this work can be linked with revision of dropping the final *e* (see pages 44–45). The **starter** activity concentrates on the -*ous* suffix. Letters are omitted in words such as *glamorous* and *humorous* (which seem to adopt the American spelling), *disastrous* and *wondrous*. An *e* is added in *righteous* and *piteous*. The **consolidation** activity asks the pupils to research the meaning and derivation of common suffixes, many of which come from Greek, Latin or Anglo-Saxon.

Meaningful choices (pages 24–25).

It is important that the pupils use the correct words (known as 'meta-language') to describe the features used in language study. This activity helps them to recognise and distinguish between homonyms, homographs and homophones. Homophones are the ones that cause the most spelling problems. The homophones *practice* and *practise* should be learned alongside *advice/advise* and *licence/license*, since in each case the -*ice* spelling denotes a noun and the -*ise* spelling denotes a verb. The difference in pronunciation between *advice* and *advise* can help the pupils to remember which is which. The pupils could look in texts they are studying to find further examples of homophones.

Rite it right (pages 26–27).

This activity looks at spelling patterns and exceptions. The **starter** activity provides a text taken from the website of a sub-group of The Simplified Spelling Society, called Reducing Irregularities in Traditional English spelling (RITE). The group aims to regularise English spelling by applying the spelling rules consistently. You could relate this to the use of simplified spelling in 'texting' for mobile phones. The **consolidation** activity encourages the pupils to investigate some of the conventions of English spelling and to realise that there are nearly always exceptions. This reinforces their understanding that they cannot always rely on the 'rules'!

Spelling strategies

Syllable search (pages 28–29). Splitting words into syllables is an excellent strategy for encouraging the pupils to look closely at words and their letter patterns. In many cases this is the simplest way of spelling longer words. The **starter** activity asks the pupils to use this strategy on some commonly misspelled words. The **consolidation** activity gives a list of *ph* words, most of which have been incorrectly split into syllables for the pupils to correct. Knowledge of prefixes and suffixes (often syllables in themselves) will help in the spelling of these words.

Memorise it (pages 30–31). This activity looks at the use of mnemonics to remember spellings. Several strategies are suggested, since different pupils will favour different approaches. The **starter** activity involves making links between the way a word looks written down, and its meaning. Many people have a visual imagination and prefer to 'see' the spelling of words. Whatever strategy works for the individual is valid. The **consolidation** and **extension** activities look at other approaches, such as finding words within words and using these to write mnemonics.

Transform it (pages 32–33). Morphology is the study of how words are formed: for example, by adding prefixes and suffixes to a root word. In the **starter** activity the pupils combine prefixes, suffixes and root words to make new words. The **consolidation** and **extension** activities reinforce this with further examples. The words in the extension activity all change their spelling in some way when a suffix is added (for example, *curious – curiosity*). The pupils will need to check their answers in a dictionary.

In the family (pages 34–35). This activity encourages the pupils to build word families by finding words derived from the same root. The **starter** activity provides three word roots from Greek and Latin. The **consolidation** activity develops this with further examples and asks the pupils to work out the meaning of the root words from the examples they have found. They should notice how the sounds of words can be different even though they belong to the same family (for example, *sign, signal*).

Trace it back (pages 36–37). This activity focuses on the derivation of words. English is a changing language which has always taken words and phrases from the languages of invaders and

Coming to a sticky end
STARTER

- Cut out the cards.
- Work out a rule for types of words that have the suffix -ible and types of words that have the suffix -able. Sort the cards into sets to help you.

Put exceptions to your rule in a separate set.

adorable	forgivable	feasible
indestructible	agreeable	indispensable
gullible	believable	manageable
movable	noticeable	collapsible
comfortable	probable	comprehensible
reasonable	contemptible	removable
convertible	responsible	changeable
credible	detestable	teachable
edible	advisable	audible
divisible	ungovernable	drinkable
unmistakable	eligible	unpronounceable

Teachers' note Split the class into small groups and give each group a copy of this page. When formulating rules, encourage the pupils to consider whether or not the root word is complete. Remind them that there will be exceptions. The pupils should also notice what happens when a vowel suffix is added to a word ending in e. Discuss that words such as *noticeable* and *manageable* keep the final e of the root word in order to retain the soft c or g sound.

Developing Literacy
Word Level
Year 9
© A & C BLACK

5. *underhand* 6. *undergrowth*; **ex-** 1. *expel* 2. *expand* 3. *exhale* 4. *execute* 5. *exclaim* 6. *excavate* 7. *extinguish* 8. *exile* 9. *extend* 10. *experiment*; **sur-** 1. *surveyor* 2. *surplus* 3. *survivor* 4. *surrender* 5. *surface*. The **consolidation** activity gives a range of different prefixes to research and provides an opportunity to develop dictionary skills. The **extension** activity highlights that the addition of a prefix does not change the spelling of the root word; this is especially relevant to commonly misspelled words such as *disappear*, *disapprove*, *irrelevant* and *misspell*.

Put an end to it! (pages 22–23).

The addition of a suffix often changes the spelling of the root word; this work can be linked with revision of dropping the final *e* (see pages 44–45). The **starter** activity concentrates on the *-ous* suffix. Letters are omitted in words such as *glamorous* and *humorous* (which seem to adopt the American spelling), *disastrous* and *wondrous*. An *e* is added in *righteous* and *piteous*. The **consolidation** activity asks the pupils to research the meaning and derivation of common suffixes, many of which come from Greek, Latin or Anglo-Saxon.

Meaningful choices (pages 24–25).

It is important that the pupils use the correct words (known as 'meta-language') to describe the features used in language study. This activity helps them to recognise and distinguish between homonyms, homographs and homophones. Homophones are the ones that cause the most spelling problems. The homophones *practice* and *practise* should be learned alongside *advice/advise* and *licence/license*, since in each case the *-ice* spelling denotes a noun and the *-ise* spelling denotes a verb. The difference in pronunciation between *advice* and *advise* can help the pupils to remember which is which. The pupils could look in texts they are studying to find further examples of homophones.

Rite it right (pages 26–27).

This activity looks at spelling patterns and exceptions. The **starter** activity provides a text taken from the website of a sub-group of The Simplified Spelling Society, called Reducing Irregularities in Traditional English spelling (RITE). The group aims to regularise English spelling by applying the spelling rules consistently. You could relate this to the use of simplified spelling in 'texting' for mobile phones. The **consolidation** activity encourages the pupils to investigate some of the conventions of English spelling and to realise that there are nearly always exceptions. This reinforces their understanding that they cannot always rely on the 'rules'!

Spelling strategies

Syllable search (pages 28–29).

Splitting words into syllables is an excellent strategy for encouraging the pupils to look closely at words and their letter patterns. In many cases this is the simplest way of spelling longer words. The **starter** activity asks the pupils to use this strategy on some commonly misspelled words. The **consolidation** activity gives a list of *ph* words, most of which have been incorrectly split into syllables for the pupils to correct. Knowledge of prefixes and suffixes (often syllables in themselves) will help in the spelling of these words.

Memorise it (pages 30–31).

This activity looks at the use of mnemonics to remember spellings. Several strategies are suggested, since different pupils will favour different approaches. The **starter** activity involves making links between the way a word looks written down, and its meaning. Many people have a visual imagination and prefer to 'see' the spelling of words. Whatever strategy works for the individual is valid. The **consolidation** and **extension** activities look at other approaches, such as finding words within words and using these to write mnemonics.

Transform it (pages 32–33).

Morphology is the study of how words are formed: for example, by adding prefixes and suffixes to a root word. In the **starter** activity the pupils combine prefixes, suffixes and root words to make new words. The **consolidation** and **extension** activities reinforce this with further examples. The words in the extension activity all change their spelling in some way when a suffix is added (for example, *curious – curiosity*). The pupils will need to check their answers in a dictionary.

In the family (pages 34–35).

This activity encourages the pupils to build word families by finding words derived from the same root. The **starter** activity provides three word roots from Greek and Latin. The **consolidation** activity develops this with further examples and asks the pupils to work out the meaning of the root words from the examples they have found. They should notice how the sounds of words can be different even though they belong to the same family (for example, *sign, signal*).

Trace it back (pages 36–37).

This activity focuses on the derivation of words. English is a changing language which has always taken words and phrases from the languages of invaders and settlers (for example, the Romans brought Latin and Greek words, and the Normans contributed French words and influences). Many of the words in the **starter** activity are from French and Latin. The pupils are encouraged to find their meanings and to discover where they originated. The **consolidation** activity shows how new words can be created to deal with new objects or processes. Many of these come from people's names.

Compare it (pages 38–39). This activity revises the comparative and superlative forms of adjectives and adverbs; the work can be linked with relevant sentence-level objectives. The **starter** activity encourages the pupils to think about how the comparatives and superlatives are formed. Short adjectives tend to use the -er and -est forms (for example, *fit – fitter – fittest*); longer adjectives and all adverbs use the *more* and *most* forms (for example, *careful – more careful – most careful*). The **consolidation** activity provides further practice, and the **extension** activity reinforces exceptions to the rules and other words commonly used incorrectly: *bad – worse – worst, dry – drier – driest, far – further, furthest, good – better – best, little – less – least, much – more – most.*

Trouble with doubles (pages 40–41). In this activity, the pupils investigate the rules for the doubling of a final consonant when a vowel suffix is added. To revise these rules, first use single-syllable examples such as *run – running* and *hit – hitting*. Practise with the pupils sounding out a variety of long and short vowel sounds. The doubling occurs in words of one syllable where a short vowel precedes a single final consonant. Ask for other examples to reinforce the rule. Exceptions are words ending in *x* (for example, *vex – vexed, tax – taxing*). In the **starter** activity the pupils are encouraged to think about why certain polysyllabic words double the final consonant and others do not. The **consolidation** and **extension** activities give a summary of the rules and ask the pupils to find examples and exceptions. If the final syllable of the word is stressed, the final consonant usually doubles when a vowel suffix is added (for example, *forget – forgetting*). Exceptions include *relax – relaxing, appeal – appealing, conceal – concealed, prefer – preference* and *refer – referee* (in the last two examples the stress moves to the first syllable of the word when the suffix is added). If the first syllable of the root word is stressed, the general rule is that the final consonant does not double (for example, *happen – happened*), but exceptions include most words ending in *l* (for example, *travel – travelled*). The pupils should also be aware of words that double their final consonant but

do not fall into any of the categories in the chart: for example, *worship – worshipping, kidnap – kidnapped, handicap – handicapped, input – inputting.*

Silent letters (pages 42–43). This activity offers revision of the rules concerning silent letters. The **starter** activity deals with the spelling patterns for the silent letters *b, k, w, t, n* and *l*. Useful words include: *thumb, climber, comb, doubt; know, knot, kneel, penknife; whole, wholly, whom, whose, wrap, wrist, rewrite; fasten, moisten, castle, bustle; hymn, column, solemn; palm, salmon, folk, almond*. The **consolidation** activity develops the work by providing four other silent letters for the pupils to investigate, with the aim of discovering rules or strategies which will be helpful in the future. Examples of words containing these silent letters are: **silent g**: *assign, benign, campaign, foreign, sign, diaphragm, phlegm, gnome, gnaw*; **silent u**: *circuit, league, guarantee, guest, buoy*; **silent h**: *wheel, whether, which, rheumatism, rhyme, rhubarb, rhythm, ghost, gherkin, Christian, choir, chemist, Thames*; **silent p**: *pneumonia, pseudonym, psychology, receipt*. The **extension** activity looks at unstressed vowels in polysyllabic words, which are often 'silent' or not pronounced clearly.

Dropping the 'e' (pages 44–45). This activity revises previous work on this spelling rule. When adding vowel suffixes, the final *e* is usually dropped to avoid creating an awkward letter combination, such as *-eing*. However, this is not generally the case with consonant suffixes (for example, *lone – lonely*). The **starter** activity provides an opportunity to investigate these rules and notice exceptions (such as *true – truly*). The **consolidation** activity provides further practice in distinguishing between vowel and consonant suffixes, and asks the pupils to formulate rules with examples. In the words in the **extension** activity, the *e* is retained for the sound of the word (for example, *gluey*), or so that the root word can be easily recognised (for example, *dyeing*).

Exchanging words (pages 46–47). A thesaurus offers an opportunity to expand vocabulary and to consider alternative words. This activity develops alphabetical and research skills as well as focusing on words with similar meanings. The **starter** activity asks the pupils to use a thesaurus to find the odd one out in sets of words. The **consolidation** and **extension** activities provide more practice in using this research tool. As a follow-up, ask the pupils to select a passage from a text they are studying and to replace some of the words with synonyms, using a thesaurus to help. They can then consider the effect this has.

Need a better checker? (pages 48–49). This activity alerts the pupils to the dangers of relying on computer spell-checkers to correct their spelling when they are word-processing. They need to be aware that although a spell-checker is a useful device, it is by no means infallible; in particular, it does not distinguish between homophones (for example, *practice/practise*). The **starter** activity provides a list of incorrectly spelled words, all of which are genuine examples. The **consolidation** activity is an exercise in proof-reading. The pupils are encouraged to distinguish between incorrect words which would be noticed by a spell-checker (for example, *honds* for *hounds*) and those which would not (for example, *hair* for *hare*). The **extension** activity reinforces this with further examples of homophones.

Look in the book (pages 50–51). This dictionary activity helps the pupils to make the most of the information they find in a dictionary entry. It also provides practice in ordering words alphabetically. The **starter** activity involves looking closely at information given in a dictionary entry, and how the different meanings of a word are conveyed. Link this with work on homonyms (see pages 24–25). The **consolidation** activity revises alphabetical order and the use of the headwords at the top of each dictionary page to speed up research. The **extension** activity encourages the pupils to familiarise themselves with their dictionary's pronunciation guide.

The birth of words (pages 52–53). This activity encourages the pupils to use etymological dictionaries to find out about the derivation of words. Etymological dictionaries can be confusing because they use abbreviations not commonly seen in standard dictionaries. However, they are valuable reference tools because they contain much more relevant information than standard dictionaries. The **starter** activity provides six entries from an etymological dictionary; the pupils are asked to work out what the words are. The answers are: (a) *feast* (b) *elbow* (c) *easel* (d) *dwell* (e) *dollar* (f) *democracy*. The **consolidation** activity continues this work by challenging the pupils to find out which of the derivations provided are true. All the derivations in the chart are correct apart from *chronicle* (*biblia khronika* meant 'books about time'). The words in the **extension** activity are all derived from people's names. Encourage the pupils to find examples of new words (or words which have recently acquired a new meaning) in texts they are studying, and to research the derivations. This could be linked with subject vocabulary, such as ICT.

High-frequency words

These activities look at strategies to spell difficult words encountered in the curriculum. The generic nature of the consolidation activity sheets enables them to be used for any words that individual pupils find difficult.

Eliminate the errors! (pages 54–55). This activity provides a reminder of the variety of spelling strategies and encourages the pupils to devise their own strategies for difficult words. The **starter** activity shows how splitting words into parts can be helpful. The pupils could share any other strategies they find useful for these words. The **consolidation** activity allows them to record the strategies they find most useful for high-frequency words.

New vocabulary (pages 56–57). This activity looks at strategies for spelling unfamiliar words. The **starter** activity takes ICT vocabulary and looks closely at possible strategies. The pupils are asked to split the words into syllables and then to look for letter patterns. The **consolidation** activity provides a way of recording their problem words and appropriate strategies.

English subject words (pages 58–59). This activity presents strategies for spelling difficult words encountered in English. The **starter** activity focuses on the Look, Say, Cover, Write and Check strategy. The **consolidation** activity encourages the pupils to decide which strategies are the most useful for particular words. Different pupils may find different kinds of vocabulary troublesome; many will have difficulty with words derived from Greek (such as *onomatopoeia*). Vocabulary from other subjects can be tackled in a similar way.

Maths words (pages 60–61). The **starter** activity focuses on high-frequency maths words that are commonly misspelled. It encourages pupils to take one word at a time and look at a range of strategies to help them spell it. The **consolidation** activity focuses on two strategies: derivation and looking for words within words. The sheet can be used in conjunction with the strategies on page 63.

Sticky subject words (pages 62–63). Subject words need particular attention, since they can be technical and difficult. In the **starter** activity, the pupils create a bank of science terms. The **consolidation** activity focuses on three strategies: splitting words into syllables, writing mnemonics, and memorising critical features using the Look, Say, Cover, Write and Check strategy.

Vowel variations
STARTER

• Read this poem aloud in a New York accent.

Toity poiple boids
Sitt'n on der coib
A'choipin and a'boipin
An' eat'n doity woims.

• How are the vowel sounds different from how we would say them?

_____

• Rewrite the poem in standard English.

• List the different ways of spelling the *ur* | vowel phoneme |.

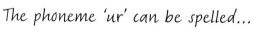

The phoneme 'ur' can be spelled...

• How many other ways are there of pronouncing this phoneme? Think about different accents you have heard.

Teachers' note Photocopy this page onto an OHT. Invite a pupil to read the poem in a New York accent; if the words are read as they are printed, the accent should emerge. Ask another pupil to write the poem in standard English on the OHT, and compare the two versions. This will show that the *ur* vowel phoneme can be spelled *ir*, *ur* or *or*. Encourage the pupils to think about how people from Scotland or Liverpool would pronounce the poem; it will become apparent that words containing the letter combinations *ir*, *ur* and *or* can be pronounced in many different ways.

Developing Literacy
Word Level
Year 9
© A & C BLACK

Vowel variations

- Listen to the *ei* **vowel phoneme** in each of these words. Use a dictionary to help you pronounce them correctly.
- List other words which contain the same vowel sound.

> The vowel sound may be spelled differently in different words. **!**

beige	*main,*
ceiling	
forfeit	
leisure	

reign	
reveille	
skein	
weird	

- Now sort the vowel sounds onto the chart below.
  Write the words on the chart and label each column.
- Add more words to the chart.

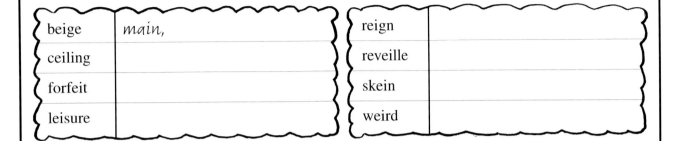

> Find as many ways as you can of spelling each vowel sound.

Sounds like ay in 'pay'	*Sounds like ee in 'bee'*				
beige *main*	*ceiling*				

NOW TRY THIS!

- Add one letter to each of these words to change the meaning and also to change the vowel sound.

> diner   fury   holy   later   pining   shining   staring   wining

Example: *diner* ⟶ *dinner*

- Write definitions to show the difference in meaning between the words in each pair.

Teachers' note Ensure that the pupils are familiar with using a dictionary's pronunciation guide. During the plenary session, discuss the difference between words such as *staring* and *starring* and revise the rules concerning the doubling of the final consonant in single-syllable words (for example, *run – running, stop – stopping*).

Plural posers

STARTER

- Write the plural of each word.
- Cut out the cards. Sort them into sets of words which change from singular to plural in the same way.

| calf | → | calves |

| loaf | → | loaves |

belief	→	blackberry →
calf	→	boy	→
cliff	→	butterfly	→
dwarf	→	cherry	→
half	→	city	→
handcuff →	family	→
hoof	→	hobby	→
knife	→	holiday	→
life	→	key	→
loaf	→	lily	→
roof	→	play	→
shelf	→	poppy	→
wife	→	ray	→
wolf	→	seventy	→
yourself →	study	→

Teachers' note Split the class into small groups and give each group a copy of this page. You could ask groups to focus either on the *f/fe* words or on the *y* words, and to write about the spelling patterns they notice. Invite feedback; discuss the rules for forming plurals and write them on the board.

Developing Literacy
Word Level
Year 9
© A & C BLACK

16

Plural posers

1. Write the plurals of these nouns.

Check your answers
in a dictionary.

army	→ _____	chief	→ _____	cuff	→ _____
elf	→ _____	herself	→ _____	life	→ _____
lorry	→ _____	penny	→ _____	ploy	→ _____
proof	→ _____	scarf	→ _____	sheaf	→ _____
thief	→ _____	tray	→ _____	worry	→ _____

2. Write the plurals of these nouns.

Check your answers
in a dictionary.

cameo	→ _____	cargo	→ _____	cuckoo	→ _____
domino	→ _____	dynamo	→ _____	echo	→ _____
grotto	→ _____	hero	→ _____	photo	→ _____
piano	→ _____	potato	→ _____	radio	→ _____
ratio	→ _____	solo	→ _____	zero	→ _____

- List four more nouns ending in *o*, and their plurals.

_____

- Write rules for making plurals of nouns ending
  in *o*. Note exceptions to your rules.

Look at the letter preceding the
final 'o'. Investigate the derivation
of the words.

_____
_____
_____

NOW TRY THIS!

- Write the plurals of these nouns.

Check your answers
in a dictionary.

commander-in-chief	deer	foot	goose	louse	man
mouse	passer-by	salmon	sheep	son-in-law	tooth	woman

- Write about the spelling patterns you notice.
- Explain why you think these words are irregular. Investigate their derivation to help.

Teachers' note Remind the pupils to take care with words ending in *o*, as some words derived
from other languages take *s* instead of *es*. Although the words in the extension activity are
exceptions to the usual rules for forming plurals, there are patterns to be found (for example,
foot – feet, goose – geese).

A blast from the past

STARTER

• Read the passage, which was written in 1470. It is based on the stories of Arthurian legend.

Whan syr Ector herde suche noyse and lyghte in the quyre of Joyous Garde, he alyght and put his hors from hym and came into the quyre. And there he sawe men synge and wepe, and all they knewe syr Ector and he knewe not them.

Glossary	
Crysten	Christian
dolour	sadness
helm	helmet
prees	praise
quyre	the choir of the church

Than went syr Bors unto syr Ector and tolde him how there laye his brother, syr Launcelot, ded. And then syr Ector threwe hys shelde, swerde, and helme from hym, and whan he behelde syr Launcelottes visage he fyl down in a swoun. And whan he waked it were harde ony tonge to telle the doleful complayntes that he made for his brother.

'A, Launcelot!' he sayd, 'thou were hede of all Crysten knyghtes! And now I dare say,' sayd syr Ector, 'thou sir Launcelot, there thou lyest, that thou were never matched of erthley knyghtes hande. And thou were the truest frende to thy lovar that ever bestrade hors, and thou were the trewest lover of a sinful man that ever loved woman, and thou were the kindest man that ever strake with swerde. And thou were the godelyest persone that ever cam emonge prees of knyghtes, and thou were the meekest man and the jentyllest that ever ete in halle emonge ladyes, and thou were the sternest knight to thy mortal foo that ever put spere in the reeste.'

Than there was wepying and dolour out of mesure.

From *Morte d'Arthur* by Sir Thomas Malory

Teachers' note Photocopy this page onto an OHT. Explain that in the passage Sir Hector finds Sir Launcelot, his brother, dead. Then invite pupils to read the passage aloud, a sentence at a time. Most of it should be easily understandable if the pupils are encouraged to read words phonetically. Ask them questions to help them work out the spelling rules of the time: for example, 'Which words are spelled the same as now? Which words are recognisable but spelled differently? How do you think they are pronounced?'

Developing Literacy
Word Level
Year 9
© A & C BLACK

A blast from the past

- Read this passage from the *Canterbury Tales* by Geoffrey Chaucer, written in about 1370.
- Underline the words you recognise as being used today, but which are spelled differently. Write the modern spelling of the words next to the poem.
- Circle any words we do not use today. Suggest possible meanings.

silly   widow

This <u>sely</u> <u>wydwe</u> and (eek) <u>hir</u> <u>doghtres</u> two   *also   her   daughters*

Herden thise hennes crie and maken wo;

And out at dores stirten they anon,

And syen the fox toward the grove gon,

And bar upon his bak the cok away;

And cryden 'Out! harrow!' and 'Weylawey!'

'Ha, ha, the fox!' and after hym they ran,

And eek with staves many another man.

Ran Colle oure dogge, and Talbot, and Gerland,

And Malkyn, with a dystaf in hir hond;

Ran cow and calf and eek the verray hogges.

So fered for the berkying of the dogges

And shoutying of the men and wommen eke,

They ronne so hem thoughte hir herte breke.

They yolleden as feendes doon in helle;

The dokes cryden as men wolde hem quelle;

The gees for feere flowen over the trees;

Out of the hyve cam the swarm of bees.

NOW TRY THIS!

- Rewrite the passage in standard English. You do not have to use rhyme.

A silly widow and her two daughters as well...

Teachers' note Ask the pupils to work in groups. Stress that there is no 'right answer' and that different groups may provide different interpretations. During the plenary session, list the words that can be identified through their sound but are spelled in a different way.

Developing Literacy
Word Level
Year 9
© A & C BLACK   **19**

Review prefixes
and their impact
on spelling and
meaning

First things first
STARTER

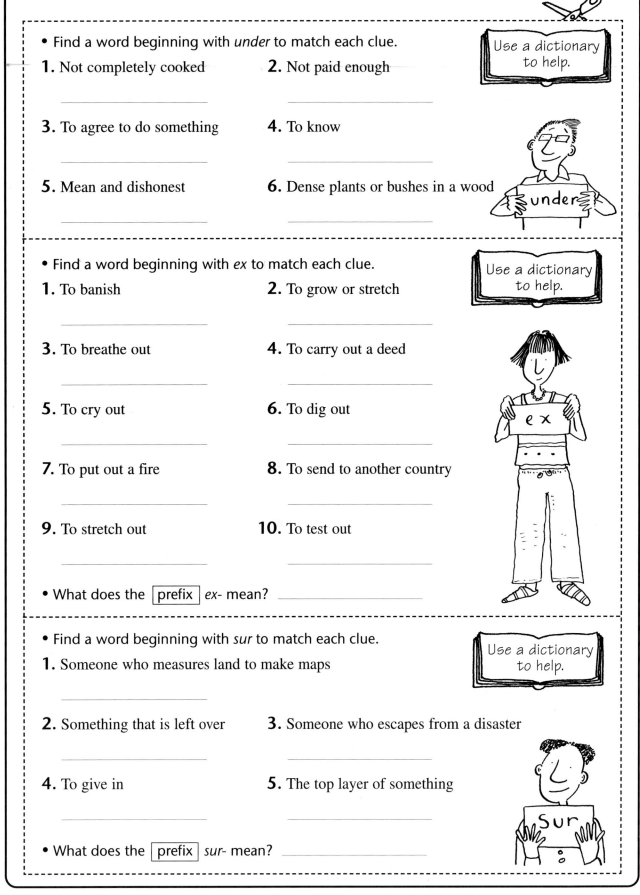

- Find a word beginning with *under* to match each clue.

Use a dictionary to help.

1. Not completely cooked

_____

2. Not paid enough

_____

3. To agree to do something

_____

4. To know

_____

5. Mean and dishonest

_____

6. Dense plants or bushes in a wood

_____

- Find a word beginning with *ex* to match each clue.

Use a dictionary to help.

1. To banish

_____

2. To grow or stretch

_____

3. To breathe out

_____

4. To carry out a deed

_____

5. To cry out

_____

6. To dig out

_____

7. To put out a fire

_____

8. To send to another country

_____

9. To stretch out

_____

10. To test out

_____

- What does the ☐ prefix ☐ *ex-* mean? _____

- Find a word beginning with *sur* to match each clue.

Use a dictionary to help.

1. Someone who measures land to make maps

_____

2. Something that is left over

_____

3. Someone who escapes from a disaster

_____

4. To give in

_____

5. The top layer of something

_____

- What does the ☐ prefix ☐ *sur-* mean? _____

Teachers' note Split the class into groups. Cut out the three cards and give a card to each group (the first card provides the easiest examples). Set a time limit of five minutes for the pupils to find as many words as possible, then bring the class together to discuss their findings. Talk about how knowledge of prefixes can help in the understanding and spelling of words. Ensure that the pupils realise the impact of the prefix on the meaning of the word.

Developing Literacy
Word Level
Year 9
© A & C BLACK

First things first

- Underline the **prefixes** in these words.
- Think of other words with the same prefixes.
- Write what you think each prefix means.

Check your answers in a dictionary.

pre-fix

Word	Other words with the same prefix	Meaning of prefix
antecedent	*antechamber, antenatal*	*before*
antipathy		
combine		
contradict		
extraordinary		
hypercritical		
international		
postpone		
prefix		
retrograde		
supersonic		
synopsis		
transmit		
ultraviolet		

NOW TRY THIS!

- Write the opposite of each word by adding the correct antonym prefix .

Antonym prefixes: un- dis- il-...

behave	colour	fortunate
honest	justice	literate
moral	polite	possible
sufficient	trust	welcome

- Does the spelling of the root word change when you add an antonym prefix? Write a rule.

Teachers' note The pupils should be able to work out the meaning of each prefix by considering the meanings of the examples they have found. During the plenary session, discuss the difference in meaning between *ante-* and *anti-*.

Developing Literacy
Word Level
Year 9
© A & C BLACK **21**

Put an end to it!

- Add the **suffix** -ous to these nouns to make adjectives.

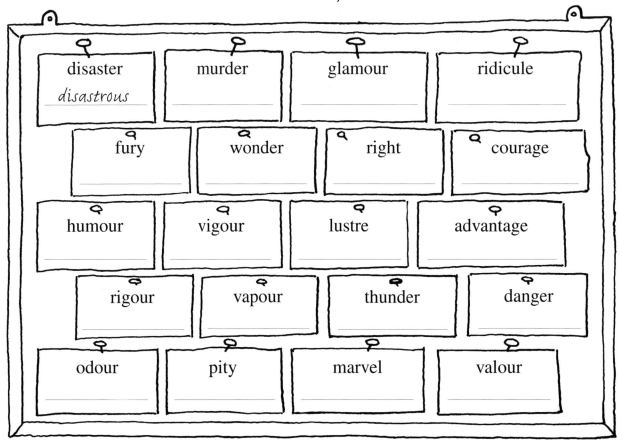

disaster	murder	glamour	ridicule
disastrous			

fury	wonder	right	courage

humour	vigour	lustre	advantage

rigour	vapour	thunder	danger

odour	pity	marvel	valour

- Write about the spelling and sound patterns you notice.

_____

_____

_____

_____

- Think of ⬚ mnemonics ⬚ to help you remember the tricky spellings. Look for words within words, or make up silly sentences using words that follow the same pattern.

  Example: *Be careful not to anger dangerous beasts!*

_____

_____

Teachers' note Photocopy this page onto an OHT. First discuss what the pupils know about suffixes and stress that the term applies to any letter or group of letters which can be added to the end of a word. Ask the pupils to say the new words ending in -ous and to listen carefully to the syllables to help them spell them correctly (for example, *dangerous* has three syllables and *wondrous* has only two, and the spelling reflects this). Encourage them to check spellings in a dictionary. Then discuss the spelling patterns and rules and write them on the OHT.

Developing Literacy
Word Level
Year 9
© A & C BLACK

22

Put an end to it!

- Find examples of words containing these **suffixes**.
- Write what the suffixes mean and which language they come from.

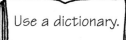

Use a dictionary.

		Words containing suffix	Meaning of suffix	Origin
Suffixes forming nouns	-ate	carbonate, nitrate	chemical compound	Latin
	-craft			
	-dom			
	-ess			
	-hood			
	-ism			
	-ship			
Suffixes forming adjectives	-able			
	-esque			
	-ful			
	-ic			
	-ish			
	-less			
Suffixes forming verbs	-en			
	-fy			
	-ise			

NOW TRY THIS!

- The suffix *-logy* or *-ology* means 'the study of'. Find words ending in *-ology* which mean the study of these subjects.

Use an etymological dictionary or the Internet.

the earth and rocks

living things

_____

crime and criminals

animals

_____

the movement of the planets and stars

the mind

_____

religions and people's beliefs

birds

_____

Teachers' note It may be helpful to group higher-attaining pupils with lower-attaining ones. Stress that they may not be able to find the same number of words for all the rows on the chart. An etymological dictionary or access to the Internet will be useful, especially for the extension activity. Encourage the pupils to find as many of the words as possible and to share their results.

Meaningful choices
STARTER

• Read the definitions.

Homonyms
• are spelled the same way
• sound the same
• have different meanings.

Example: wave/wave

Homographs
• are spelled the same way
• sound different
• have different meanings.

Example: lead/lead

Homophones
• sound the same
• are spelled differently
• have different meanings.

Example: sail/sale

• Cut out the cards.
• Each word is a homonym, a homograph or a homophone (or it may be more than one of these). Write which it is and write the other word in the pair.
• Sort the cards according to whether they are homonyms, homographs or homophones.

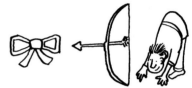

bow/bow
homonym and
homograph

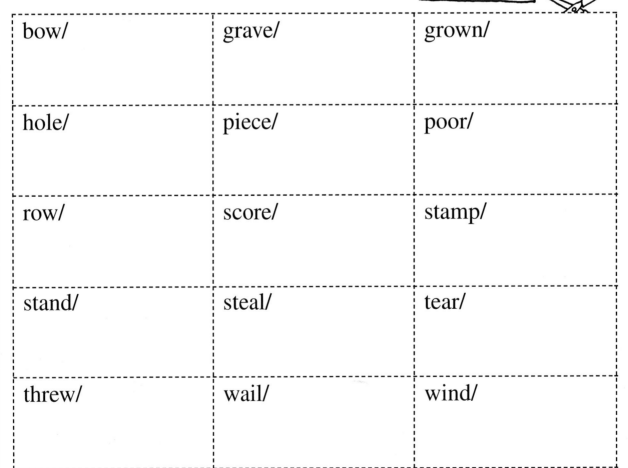

bow/	grave/	grown/
hole/	piece/	poor/
row/	score/	stamp/
stand/	steal/	tear/
threw/	wail/	wind/

Teachers' note Ask the pupils to work in pairs and give each pair a copy of this page. Explain that some of the words on the cards may fall into more than one category (for example, *bow* is both a homonym and a homograph). Encourage the pupils to sort the words and to explain the different meanings of the homonyms, homographs and homophones. They could show the meanings by using the words in sentences. Discuss strategies such as mnemonics which can help them to remember how to spell homophones.

Developing Literacy
Word Level
Year 9
© A & C BLACK

Meaningful choices

- Find **homophones** for these words.
- Use a dictionary to check you are sure of all the meanings.

There might be more than one homophone. Find as many as you can.

!

Word	Homophones
aloud	*allowed*
breaking	
cite	
flue	
lone	

Word	Homophones
palate	
peer	
shear	
suede	
they're	

- Find at least four more pairs of homophones.

stare/stair, _____

_____

The following words mean different things when they are pronounced in different ways.

- Write the words in sentences, to show the different meanings.

read _____

_____

record _____

_____

rebel _____

_____

permit _____

_____

- Are the words homographs, homophones or homonyms? Explain why.

_____

NOW TRY THIS!

- Write two sentences for each of these words. Use the word as a noun in one sentence and as a verb in another.

coach	finish	fire	loom
mint	play	ring	strike

You're fired!

- Are the words homographs, homophones or homonyms? Explain why.

Teachers' note Encourage the pupils to practise using homophones in context to reinforce their spellings. During the plenary session, you could ask the pupils to try using homophones in incorrect contexts to make funny sentences (for example, *Keep your hare under control with new Salon Style shampoo.*)

Rite it right

- Read this extract of text from a website, which was written by a group of people who want to simplify spelling patterns.
- What spelling patterns can you see in the text?

 RITE HELPS U RITE RITE

But if there has been all this suport for spelling chainges, wy hav there not been enny chainges?

We think the reeson is that chainges in the past ment that, firstly, peeple wood hav to lern their spelling all over again and secondly, our wunderful traditional spelling would be lost forevver.

This is where RITE is difrent.

RITE meerly consollidates the best in our Traditional Spelling.

This meens that peeple wil not hav to lern their spelling all over again.

This meens that we wil not loos our Traditional Spelling.

We ar an e-groop cumming from the SSS (Simplified Spelling Society, founded 1909), and we hav been discussing and voting on proposals tu elimminate exeptions in english spelling. As the name RITE (Reducing Iregularities in Traditional English spelling) ses, it dusnt chainge english rules, it just aplys them consistently. Try riting it. If in dout u can always use Traditional Spelling. The RITE-Groop dusnt propose a spelling poleece force ennyway...

If u want tu no wat RITE basically is, heer it is: RITE cuts redundant letters *(hed, dout, exept)* and reggularizes short vowels *(and, sed, it, on, luv, havving, matter, enny, better, wimmen, difficult, offen, possible, munny, suddenly)*, long vowels *(made, grate, like, rite, home, rode, huge, buty)* and three consonants: *f* for the *f* sound *(far, grafic, laf)*, *x* for the *ks* sound *(box, axept)* and *z* for the *z* sound *(advize, bizzy)*.

U mite soon realize that there ar stil inconsistencies in RITE, e.g. *air/scare/ there, out* but *down*, etc. RITE is stil develloping, and u can take part in it.

If u want tu delv further intu RITE acording tu the ballots we hav had so far, just clik wun of the RITE links belo...

From www.ritespel.org

Simplified Spelling Society

Make nu frendz!

Fil Lueez Peet Ema

Teachers' note Photocopy this page onto an OHT. First explain that for many years there has been a debate about 'simplified spelling' – that is, how we could change English spelling to remove some of the idiosyncrasies and irregularities. Read the passage with the whole class and discuss whether the argument makes sense. Look at the spelling of the words in the passage and make a list of the conventions and rules which are being proposed to help simplify spelling.

Developing Literacy
Word Level
Year 9
© A & C BLACK

Rite it right

For nearly every pattern in English spelling, there are exceptions.

• Complete the chart to show this.

Write here words with the same sound spelled in a different way.

Words	Spelling pattern	Spelling exceptions
state, lame, mane	a-e	*weight, fail, beige, gauge*
metal, denial, petal	al	
start, farm, card	ar	
fare, stare, hare	are	
ordinary, cautionary	ary	
stay, hay, play	ay	
set, men, led	e	
tree, seed, beetle	ee	
lessen, worsen, happen	en	
letter, painter, writer	er	
fish, friend, fine	f	
kite, shine, pipe	i-e	
stone, home, wrote	o-e	
soon, too, boot	oo	
bore, snore, wore	ore	
trout, loud, joust	ou	
sun, hunt, mud	u	
youth, yes, you	y	

NOW TRY THIS!

• Choose five words on this page that you find difficult to spell.
• Think of strategies for remembering how to spell the words. You could try these methods.

Find a word within the word: *les**son***

Write or draw a **mnemonic**: *<u>We</u> are the same <u>weight</u>.*

Investigate the **derivation** of the word: *phase – 'ph' words are derived from Greek*

Use the Look, Say, Cover, Write and Check strategy.

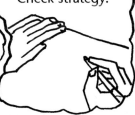

Split the word into **phonemes** or **syllables**: *b/ei/ge   de/ni/al*

Teachers' note Stress that the pupils may not be able to complete the entire chart. They could look in class texts for exceptions to the spelling patterns. During the plenary session, discuss problem areas of the chart and encourage the pupils to fill in any gaps. Ask them to share their mnemonics.

Developing Literacy
Word Level
Year 9
© A & C BLACK 27

Syllable search
STARTER

- Draw lines to split each word into **syllables**.
- Write the word out again. Look out for any tricky parts in each syllable.

Remember, each syllable must contain a vowel or a 'y'.

a c/c o m/m o/d a/t i o n
accommodation

r e c o m m e n d

a l t o g e t h e r

b u s i n e s s

p o s s e s s i o n

b a c h e l o r

s e p a r a t e

g u a r a n t e e

e n v i r o n m e n t

o p p o r t u n i t y

q u e s t i o n n a i r e

v e h i c l e

p r i v i l e g e

c e m e t e r y

d e s c e n d a n t

i n d i s p e n s a b l e

p e r s e v e r a n c e

p r e j u d i c e

f l u o r e s c e n t

a n n i h i l a t e

Teachers' note Ask the pupils to work in pairs and give each pair a copy of this page. Alternatively, you could cut out the words and give them to individuals or groups depending on their level of attainment. The pupils should say the words aloud and sound out the syllables. Remind them that there are different ways of splitting words into syllables (for example, *ac/com/mo/da/tion, acc/omm/od/a/tion*). Tricky words can be learned using the Look, Say, Cover, Write and Check strategy.

Developing Literacy
Word Level
Year 9
© A & C BLACK

Syllable search

These *ph* words have been split into **syllables**. Some are incorrect.
- Mark whether the syllables are correct or incorrect. Write a corrected version where appropriate.
- Write the whole word again.

Word	✔ or ✘	Corrected syllables	Write the word
apo / stro / phe	✘	a / po / stro / phe	apostrophe
cat / a / str / oph / e			
ce / not / a / ph			
di / a / phragm			
ele / ph / ant			
epit / aph			
me / ta / phor			
micro / phone			
ne / phew			
or / ph / an			
pa / ra / graph			
pa / ra / pher / nalia			
phar / macy			
ph / ea / sa / nt			
phe / no / men / on			
phob / ia			
phr / ase			
phy / sio / the / rapy			
phy / si / que			
sp / he / re			

NOW TRY THIS!
- Look carefully at the words on the chart. Think of other strategies to help you remember how to spell them.

Example: *Derivation of 'microphone':*
  micro = small
  phone = sound (from Greek)

Teachers' note Encourage the pupils to sound out the words to help them identify the syllables. Beating out a rhythm sometimes helps. Ask them to check that each syllable contains a vowel or a *y* before they write the whole word again. There are various correct ways of splitting the words: for example, *a/po/stro/phe, ap/os/troph/e*.

Memorise it
STARTER

Mnemonics can help you to remember the difficult parts of words.
All these words contain a tricky *y*, where the *y* acts as a vowel.

• Use the *y* in each word to create a visual mnemonic.
• Make up a written mnemonic beneath each picture.

EG**Y**PTIAN

Y did the ancient EgYptians build pyramids?

L**Y**RICAL

RH**Y**THM

H**Y**PNOTISE

S**Y**MMETRY

G**Y**MNASIUM

Teachers' note Give each pupil a photocopy of this page. Stress that there are no 'right answers' and that the pupils should use whatever method works for them. Their mnemonics can be as silly as they like. Bring the class together after about five minutes and discuss their ideas. Ask the pupils to think about whether they find visual or written mnemonics more effective.

Developing Literacy
Word Level
Year 9
© A & C BLACK

Memorise it

Finding words within words is a useful starting point for writing **mnemonics**.

• Find words within these words.

Word	Words inside
because	*be, cause, use*
business	
comfortable	
environment	
existence	
industrial	

Word	Words inside
ingredient	
knowledge	
manufacture	
miscellaneous	
pleasant	
practice	

• Make up mnemonics using the words you have found.

The cat found the <u>table</u> to be most comfor<u>table</u>.

NOW TRY THIS!

There are other kinds of strategies you can use to memorise difficult words.

while
Q. What says 'hello' in 'while'?
A. The 'hi' in the middle.

necessary
It is necessary to have one collar (C) and two socks (S).

rhythm
<u>R</u>hythm <u>H</u>elps <u>Y</u>our <u>T</u>oes <u>H</u>op <u>M</u>agically.

A – double C – O – double M – O – D – A – T – I – O – N

accommodation

• Try using these strategies with the following words.

across	embarrass	government	heir
intelligent	listener	privilege	temperature

Teachers' note Remind the pupils that *practice* is a noun and *practise* is a verb. Their mnemonics should aim to help them remember this distinction. Stress that they may find some of these methods more useful than others, and that they should identify which they prefer. Their mnemonics can be as silly as they like.

Transform it

STARTER

Morphology is the study of how words are formed: for example, by adding prefixes and suffixes to root words.

- Cut out the cards. Use them to build as many new words as possible.

- List your new words. Underline them to show which part of the word is the root word, prefix and suffix.

> ! Watch out for changes to the spelling of the root word when you add a prefix or suffix.

Underline the root words in blue.
Underline the prefixes in red.
Underline the suffixes in green.

| un | help | ful |

open	fresh	scope
ful	un	place
appoint	micro	ology
ing	appear	ed
play	help	tele
dis	d	ment
approve	measure	phone
s	grace	re

Teachers' note Split the class into groups and give each group a copy of this page. Introduce the term 'morphology'. Explain that 'morph' means 'change', so morphology involves changing words by adding prefixes and suffixes. Challenge the pupils to make as many words as possible within five minutes. Remind them that they may need to change the spelling of the root word (for example, by dropping the final *e*). Invite the pupils to share their words, and discuss any changes to the spelling of the root words.

Developing Literacy
Word Level
Year 9
© A & C BLACK

Transform it

- Add as many **suffixes** as possible to these **root words**. Write the new words.

Check your answers in a dictionary.

Root word	New words with suffixes
hard	*hardly, hardness, harden, hardy, hardship, harder*
mind	
press	
colour	
excite	
consider	
behave	
construct	
electric	
child	
nine	

- Underline the root words in each of the new words you have made. Think about any changes to the spelling of the root word.

- Where possible, add **prefixes** to the words you have made. List the new words with prefixes.

reminder,

NOW TRY THIS!

- Choose suffixes from the notepad to add to these words.

Check your spelling carefully – these are tricky!

Suffixes

-ous -ition -ance -y
-ity -ation -ty

| curious | disaster | exclaim | four | maintain |
| monster | pronounce | remember | repeat | winter |

Teachers' note Stress that the consolidation activity is an investigation, and that there are many possible answers. During the plenary session, highlight the spelling rules (for example, the final *e* of a root word is usually dropped when a vowel suffix is added but not when a consonant suffix is added).

In the family
STARTER

The words in a ⌐word family¬ all come from the same ⌐word root¬ .

• Find words belonging to these word families. Write them in the grids.

Use a dictionary to help.

pathos is Greek for 'feeling' or 'suffering'

			p	a	t	h	e	t	i	c		
			p	a	t	h						
			p	a	t	h						
			p	a	t	h						
			p	a	t	h						
			p	a	t	h						

ped comes from **pes/pedis**, Latin for 'foot'

		p	e	d					
		p	e	d					
		p	e	d					
		p	e	d					
		p	e	d					
		p	e	d					

ject comes from **jactare**, Latin for 'to throw'

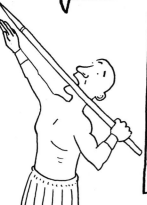

		j	e	c	t					
		j	e	c	t					
		j	e	c	t					
		j	e	c	t					
		j	e	c	t					
		j	e	c	t					

Teachers' note Photocopy this page onto an OHT. Discuss the grids one at a time and invite the pupils to write words on the OHT. They can use dictionaries to help them find suitable words. In each case, stress the meaning of the word root and how this can help with the development of the word family. When the OHT is complete, discuss the spelling patterns of the words within the same family.

Developing Literacy
Word Level
Year 9
© A & C BLACK

In the family

Many English words come from Latin **root words**.

- Write at least four words in each family, coming from the same Latin root word.

- Think about the meanings of your words. Write what you think the Latin root word means (they are all verbs).

Use a dictionary to help.

	s	i	g	n	a	t	u	r	e		
	s	i	g	n							
	s	i	g	n							
	s	i	g	n							

Latin root word: *signare*

Meaning: *to mark*

	s	e	c	t							
	s	e	c	t							
	s	e	c	t							
	s	e	c	t							

Latin root word: *secare*

Meaning: _____

	f	i	n	i	t						
	f	i	n	i	t						
	f	i	n	i	t						
	f	i	n	i	t						

Latin root word: *finire*

Meaning: _____

	s	p	e	c	t						
	s	p	e	c	t						
	s	p	e	c	t						
	s	p	e	c	t						

Latin root word: *specere*

Meaning: _____

NOW TRY THIS!

- Make **word families** containing these **word roots** derived from Greek and Latin.

- Write what you think the word root means.

| astro | bene | chron |
| medic | photo | script |

- Explain how word families can help you with spelling.

Teachers' note Make sure that the pupils check their answers in a dictionary so that they can feed back their answers more profitably during the plenary session. They should be aware of the characteristics shared by words in the same family, and also any words in the family which involve changes in spelling to the root word.

Trace it back
STARTER

- Join each word or phrase to its meaning.
- Make notes on the **derivation** of the words or phrases, and the languages from which they are derived.

Use a dictionary.

Words/phrases	Meanings
ad infinitum	genuine; made in good faith
anorak	one more time!
au revoir	a warm, waterproof jacket
bona fide	on the way
carte blanche	going on for ever; endlessly
en route	goodbye for now
encore	a system of unarmed combat
fiancé	a list of food and drink
hors-d'œuvre	complete authority to make decisions
karate	the first course of a meal
menu	a man engaged to be married
nom de plume	something that does not follow on logically
non sequitur	a private conversation between two people
par excellence	examination of body after death
persona non grata	a fictitious name used by an author
post-mortem	an unacceptable or unwelcome person
siesta	the existing state of affairs
status quo	the best example of its kind
tête-à-tête	order or relations reversed
vice versa	an afternoon rest

Teachers' note Ask the pupils to work in pairs and give each pair a copy of this page. Some of these words will be known to the pupils, but many will not. An etymological dictionary or access to the Internet will be useful for research. Explain that many of the less common foreign words and phrases are usually set in italics when they are used in English.

Developing Literacy
Word Level
Year 9
© A & C BLACK

Trace it back

• Find the meanings of these words and explain their origins.

Use a dictionary.

Bring me a piece of meat between two slices of bread!

Word	Meaning	Origin
sandwich	*Two or more slices of bread with a filling between*	*The Earl of Sandwich's favourite meal while at the gambling table*
diesel		
jovial		
pasteurise		
dunce		
galvanise		
limerick		
bowdlerise		
martial		
mesmerise		
tantalise		

NOW TRY THIS!

• What number is suggested by each of these words?
• List other words which use the same **derivation**.

decade	octave	unique	sextet
trio	century	quartet	kilogram

Teachers' note Most of the words on the chart are derived from proper nouns. The pupils will need to research the meanings using reference sources; many standard dictionaries will contain the information, but an etymological dictionary will be more useful. The Internet will also provide useful pointers.

Compare it
STARTER

- Cut out the cards.
- Pick a card and complete it, using the [positive], [comparative] and [superlative] forms of the words in sentences.

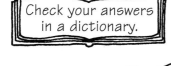

Check your answers in a dictionary.

Example:

strong
Word class: *adjective*

Positive: *This is a strong rope.*

Comparative: *Mine is stronger than yours.*

Superlative: *This is the strongest of all.*

---

funny	**careful**
Word class: _____	Word class: _____
Positive: _____	Positive: _____
Comparative: _____	Comparative: _____
Superlative: _____	Superlative: _____
good	**slowly**
Word class: _____	Word class: _____
Positive: _____	Positive: _____
Comparative: _____	Comparative: _____
Superlative: _____	Superlative: _____
thankful	**tunefully**
Word class: _____	Word class: _____
Positive: _____	Positive: _____
Comparative: _____	Comparative: _____
Superlative: _____	Superlative: _____
fit	**lovely**
Word class: _____	Word class: _____
Positive: _____	Positive: _____
Comparative: _____	Comparative: _____
Superlative: _____	Superlative: _____
willingly	**bad**
Word class: _____	Word class: _____
Positive: _____	Positive: _____
Comparative: _____	Comparative: _____
Superlative: _____	Superlative: _____

38

Teachers' note Split the class into small groups and give each group a copy of this page. First revise word classes, including adjectives and adverbs. Encourage the pupils to look out for changes in spelling (for example, *y* changing to *i* in *lovelier*). Discuss the different ways in which the comparatives and superlatives are formed, and which words follow which pattern. Review the rules that can help with the spelling of such words in the future.

Developing Literacy
Word Level
Year 9
© A & C BLACK

Compare it

• Write the **comparative** and **superlative** forms of the words.

Positive	Comparative	Superlative
beautiful	*more beautiful*	*most beautiful*
big		
cool		
cunning		
dangerous		
enthusiastic		
grey		
hungry		
joyful		
lively		
noisy		
odd		
pleasant		
sad		
stubborn		
wide		

• What patterns can you find in how the comparative and superlative forms are made, and how the spelling changes? Write some rules.

! Try comparing shorter words and longer words.

_____

_____

_____

_____

NOW TRY THIS!

• Write the comparative and superlative forms of these words. Check your answers in a dictionary.

Be careful! Most are irregular.

| bad | dry | far | good | little | much |

Teachers' note Remind the pupils that the words will not all follow the same pattern. During the plenary session, ask the pupils to share and evaluate the rules they have written. Discuss the exceptions to the rules given in the extension activity and ask the pupils to think of strategies for remembering them.

Trouble with doubles

STARTER

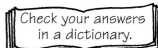

Check your answers in a dictionary.

- Cut out the cards.
- Pick a card and choose suitable **suffixes** to add to the word. List the new words you make.

Suffixes

-able -ee -ty
-er -ing -ment
-ence -some -ed
-est -ful -en
-ness

Think about whether you need to double the final letter of the root word, and why. It will be helpful to consider:
- whether you are adding a **vowel suffix** or a **consonant suffix**
- the number of syllables in the root word
- the final letter of the root word and the letter preceding it
- which syllable the stress falls upon.

swimming   swimmer

swim	commit	common
enrol	cut	offer
happen	hope	forget
glad	cruel	occur
open	land	prefer
gallop	benefit	quarrel

Teachers' note Split the class into small groups and give each group a copy of this page. Before beginning, briefly revise the doubling of letters when adding vowel suffixes (see page 8). Explain that in words of more than one syllable, where the stress (or emphasis) falls can affect whether or not the final consonant doubles when a suffix is added. Encourage them to notice that the doubling also depends on whether a vowel suffix or a consonant suffix is being added (the addition of a consonant suffix usually has no effect on the spelling of a root word).

Developing Literacy
Word Level
Year 9
© A & C BLACK

Trouble with doubles

- The chart shows when to double the final consonants of words. Write at least four more examples for each rule.

Rule Double the final consonant when you add a vowel suffix to...	Examples	
	Word	**Word with vowel suffix**
Words with one syllable • a word with a short vowel sound and one final consonant.	run	running
Words with more than one syllable • a word ending in a single vowel followed by one consonant, where the stress falls on the final syllable.	regret	regretted
• a word ending in a single vowel followed by *l*.	travel	traveller

NOW TRY THIS!

- List any exceptions to the rules.

Rule Double the final consonant when you add a vowel suffix to...	Exceptions
Words with one syllable • a word with a short vowel sound and one final consonant.	vex – vexing
Words with more than one syllable • a word ending in a single vowel followed by one consonant, where the stress falls on the final syllable.	destroy – destroying
• a word ending in a single vowel followed by *l*.	parallel – paralleled

Teachers' note Some pupils may need to revise identifying where the stress falls in words. Encourage them to practise this by saying words out loud; ask them to place the stress on different syllables in turn and to decide which sounds most natural. When the pupils have completed the sheet, they should file it for future reference.

Silent letters

STARTER

• Complete the chart to show the spelling patterns for [silent letters].

Give at least three more examples.

!

Silent letter	Spelling pattern	Examples
b	Occurs after ____ or before ____ at the end of a syllable or word.	*plumber,*
k	Occurs before ____	*knitting,*
w		*who,*
t		*listen,*
n		*autumn,*
l		*walk,*

Teachers' note Photocopy this page onto an OHT. Ask the pupils to contribute words containing the silent letters, and then to use the examples to help them formulate rules. Once the chart is complete, you could photocopy it for the pupils so that they can file it for future reference. See page 8 for useful words.

Developing Literacy
Word Level
Year 9
© A & C BLACK

Silent letters

- List words containing these **silent letters**.

Silent g
align
gnome

Silent u
biscuit
guide

Silent h
whale
rhinoceros

Silent p
pneumatic
psalm

- Use a dictionary to find out the languages from which the words are derived.
- Look at the spelling patterns and derivations. Write strategies to help with the spelling of words containing these silent letters.

Silent g: _____

_____

_____

Silent u: _____

_____

_____

Silent h: _____

_____

Silent p: _____

_____

NOW TRY THIS!

Sometimes | unstressed vowels | are 'silent' or not pronounced clearly.

- Fill in the unstressed vowels in these words.

| alc___hol | ben___fit | bus___ness | categ___ry | compr___mise |
| conf___rence | desp___rate | diff___rence | fright___ning | int___rested |

- List other words which have the same spelling problem. Circle the unstressed vowels.

Teachers' note Explain, using an example, that unstressed vowels can make words difficult to spell. The pupils may find it helpful to 'spell-speak' the words by sounding out every letter in an exaggerated way (for example, *des-PER-ate*). Encourage clear pronunciation at all times.

Dropping the 'e'
STARTER

• Some of the word endings in this passage are incorrect. Underline and correct the errors.

Dear Sophie,

adventurous

I hope you're feeling <u>adventure</u> because I've just had the most amaze offer.

You remember that amuse man we met on holiday – you had an argue with him – (what terrible behave)! He was celebrate his retirement by move to Venice. This was a very dare thing to do for someone his age.

Anyway, after drive all the way from Manchester – what an excite adventure! – he was hope to learn Italian in a week. He clearly had a great image! Now he has written to me, invite us to stay at his Venetian palace. He obviously took a like to us!

You may feel a bit nerve about going to stay with a stranger, and my parents took a little persuade. He is renovate the palace and needs all the help he can get. My brother says I'm being ridicule and that the whole thing sounds scare, but I'm sense, aren't I?

So, if you want to come, telephone me and don't be bore. This is true an offer we can't refuse. He may be use us as cheap labour but it will be a free holiday. I'm write to him tomorrow so I'll need your reply by then.

Talk soon,

Vicky x ☺

Teachers' note Photocopy this page onto an OHT. Tell the pupils that all the words which are used incorrectly end in *e*, and that the correct words can be found by adding a suffix. In doing so, the spelling of the word may change. Invite the pupils to underline the errors and write the corrected words in the spaces between the lines. When they have completed the passage, discuss whether the final *e* is always dropped, and whether there is a difference between the addition of a vowel suffix or a consonant suffix.

Developing Literacy
Word Level
Year 9
© A & C BLACK

Dropping the 'e'

• List as many **suffixes** as you can. Sort them into **vowel suffixes** and **consonant suffixes**.

Vowel suffixes

-ed,

Consonant suffixes

-ment,

• Complete the chart to show when to drop the final *e*.

Give examples using all your suffixes, if possible.

!

Rule	Examples	Any exceptions
1. Keep the final *e* before _____ suffixes, such as _____ .		
2. Drop the final *e* before _____ suffixes, such as _____ .		

NOW TRY THIS!

• Discuss with a partner why these spellings occur.

acreage	ageing	dyeing
gluey	likeable	singeing

• List any other similar examples you can think of.

Teachers' note Revise what is meant by a vowel suffix and a consonant suffix, and encourage the pupils to brainstorm as many as possible (it may be useful for them to do this in groups). Ensure that they are aware of exceptions to the rules. When the pupils have completed the sheet, they should file it for future reference.

Developing Literacy Word Level Year 9 © A & C BLACK 45

Exchanging words
STARTER

In each bubble, three of the words have similar meanings.

• Circle the odd one out.

Use a thesaurus.

artifice
premise
stratagem
ruse

buyer
customer
purchaser
vendor

concise
succinct
subservient
terse

gullible
frank
trustful
credulous

obligation
contract
bequest
covenant

pity
sympathise
commiserate
condone

obsessed
obdurate
stubborn
refractory

supercilious
servile
deferential
sycophantic

talkative
loquacious
voluble
ingenuous

vilify
dissimulate
disparage
malign

Teachers' note Ask the pupils to work in pairs and give each pair a copy of this page. Explain that it is not necessary to look up all the words in the set, since a thesaurus provides all the words with similar meanings under one entry. Discuss any other words the pupils have found with similar meanings to those in the bubbles.

Developing Literacy
Word Level
Year 9
© A & C BLACK

Exchanging words

• Join the words with similar meanings.

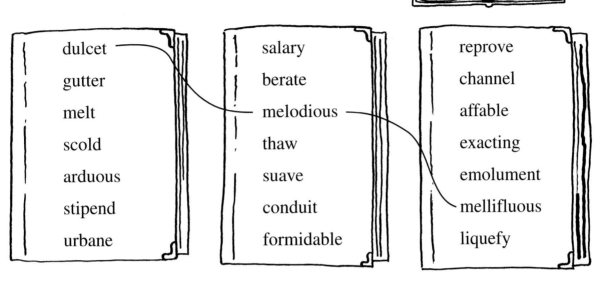

Use a thesaurus to help.

dulcet	salary	reprove
gutter	berate	channel
melt	melodious	affable
scold	thaw	exacting
arduous	suave	emolument
stipend	conduit	mellifluous
urbane	formidable	liquefy

• Use a thesaurus to find three alternatives for each of the following words.

Word	Alternatives
intelligent	*perceptive,*
atrocious	
dilemma	
enthusiastic	
omen	
to ask	
to conciliate	
to walk	

NOW TRY THIS!

• Rewrite these texts more simply. Use a thesaurus and dictionary to help.

Refrain from expectoration.

His decease was precipitated by over-consumption of intoxicating beverages and by excessive nicotine inhalation.

The increase of exchequer expenditure on conventional weapon research has necessitated the diversion of financial resources from education and social services.

Teachers' note The pupils could complete this activity in groups. Encourage them to try using the alternative words they find in sentences. As a further extension, you could ask the pupils to find as many alternatives as possible for *big* (for example, *enormous, elephantine, gargantuan*) and *said* (for example, *spoke, enquired, muttered*).

Need a better checker?

- Imagine you are a computer spell-checker. Suggest which word you think the person intended to write.

File Edit View Insert

Not in dictionary	Suggestions
abuot	*about*
anser	
becos	
coredor	
exspensiv	
fizics	
heting	
hosptall	
itaresting	
noys	
peeopol	
pitchur	
prakts	
sicors	
spelln	
streased	
tempricur	
vegitatin	
wrten	
yooshaly	

Teachers' note Give each pupil a copy of this page. Ask the pupils to sound out the words and to guess what they are meant to represent. They should check the correct spellings in a dictionary if necessary. If ICT resources are available, the pupils could try typing the words into a computer spell-checker to see the range of options given.

Developing Literacy
Word Level
Year 9
© A & C BLACK

Need a better checker?

- Read this passage carefully. There are many typing errors.
- Underline in blue the incorrect words which are likely to be noticed by a spell-checker.
- Underline in red the incorrect words which are *not* likely to be noticed by a spell-checker.
- Write the correct words in the spaces above.

The honds now past the rivulet, and persued the fotsteps of the hair; five horsmen atempted to leep over, three of whom suceeded, and two where in the atempt throne from there sadles into the water; their commpanions, and they're own horses to, proceded after their sport, and left their freinds and riders to envoke the asistance of Fortune, or employ the more active meens of strenth and agillity for their delivrance.

The hunds we're know very little behind their poor, realing, stagering pray, wich feinting almost at every step, crorled throuh the wood, and got round to the plaice where Fanny stood, and hid befor beeing overtaken by its enemys and avoyded being torne to peeces.

From *Joseph Andrews* by Henry Fielding

- Explain why a spell-checker will not identify certain incorrect words.

_____

_____

NOW TRY THIS!

- For each of these words, find a **homophone** or a similar-sounding word.

  accept   affect   hoarse   practice   principal

- Write sentences containing the words to show the correct context in which each should be used.

Teachers' note Revise homophones and emphasise that spell-checkers do not take homophones into account because they cannot assess the use and meaning of a word in context. During the plenary session, remind the pupils that they should always read and check their written work before publishing, even if they have put it through a computer spell-checker.

Look in the book
STARTER

• Read this extract from a dictionary.

house (hows) *n.* **1.** a building for dwelling in; a dwelling-place. **2.** a hotel, restaurant, club etc. **3.** a family or dynasty. **4.** a legislative body (House of Commons, House of Lords, House of Representatives etc.). **5.** the audience in a place of entertainment, a theatre, etc. *vb.* **6.** to provide with accommodation. **7.** to protect by covering. **8.** to store.

• Write your own dictionary definitions for these words, without looking in a dictionary.

Think of as many different uses of the words as you can. !

head

line

Teachers' note Photocopy this page onto an OHT. Read the dictionary entry for *house* with the whole class and discuss the information it gives. Review the guide to pronunciation (*hows*) and the meanings of the abbreviations used. Then ask groups within the class to write similar dictionary entries for *head* and *line*. Invite the pupils to write their definitions on the OHT, and encourage constructive criticism from the rest of the class. Discuss the variety of meanings and how these can be made clear to the reader.

Developing Literacy
Word Level
Year 9
© A & C BLACK

Look in the book

1. 'Grapheme' and 'gravity' are the first and last words on a dictionary page.

• Underline the words you would find on that page.

• Write them on the page in alphabetical order.

gratuity	gravure	graphic
grass	grapevine	grapple
graviton	gravely	gravy
grapeshot	graphite	grasp
grasshopper	grave	gratify
grazing	gravitation	grate

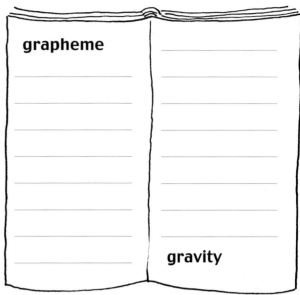

grapheme

gravity

2. 'Rainy' and 'randomise' are the first and last words on a dictionary page.

• Underline the words you would find on that page.

• Write them on the page in alphabetical order.

Ramadan	range	ramify
random	rally	rambutan
rainwater	raisin	ramekin
ramshackle	rancid	raise
rainbow	rakish	rampage
rambunctious	ragged	rank

rainy

randomise

NOW TRY THIS!

• Make sure you understand your dictionary's pronunciation guide. Check how to pronounce the following words.

advertisement	corps	courtesy	gauge	indictment
infamous	inventory	lieutenant	restaurant	wrath

Teachers' note Discuss how the headwords at the top of a dictionary page tell you which words you can expect to find on that page. Encourage the pupils to discuss any difficulties they had in ordering the words: for example, where the first four or five letters of the words were the same.

The birth of words

STARTER

- Cut out the cards. They are entries from an etymological dictionary.
- Look carefully at the information.
- Write the word you think each entry is describing.

(a) _____

n. O.F. *feste* (F. *fête*) L. *festa,* festal ceremonies, neut. pl. of *festus,* festal – a festivity, cogn. with *feria,* fair. A religious anniversary to be kept with rejoicing; a banquet. To fare sumptuously, regale oneself.

(b) _____

n. O.E. *elboga, elnboga,* f. *eln,* forearm + *boga,* a bow, a bending. Ger. *ell(en)bogen.* The outer part of the joint of the arm. To force one's way through with this part.

(c) _____

n. Du. *ezel,* ass; Ger. *esel,* ass. c.f. the sim. use of *horse.* A frame to support a picture which is being painted.

(d) _____

vi. O.E. *dwellan,* to mislead, delay, to go astray. O. Teut. root *dewl-, dwal-, dwol-,* to be torpid, to cease, to err. Formerly to mislead; to hinder; to tarry. To continue for a time in a place or condition; to reside, live.

(e) _____

n. L.G. *daler*; H.G. *taler, thaler,* shortened form of *Joachimst(h)aler,* (coin) of the valley of Joachim in Bohemia, where there were silver mines. The English name for the German *thaler,* a coin of varying value; currency of USA and Canada.

(f) _____

n. G. *demos,* the people + *kratia,* rule, f. *kratos,* power. Government by the people; a state so governed; the common people (in reference to their political power).

Teachers' note Read the examples with the pupils and ensure that they understand the abbreviations. Give help with the less common abbreviations: *f.* = from; *cogn.* = cognate (related to); *c.f.* = confer (compare); *O. Teut.* = Old Teutonic; *L.G.* = Low German; *H.G.* = High German. Ask the pupils to work out the words from the clues. They can then check their answers using an etymological dictionary. Invite the pupils to explain how they knew the answers.

Developing Literacy
Word Level
Year 9
© A & C BLACK

52

The birth of words

- Find out which of these are true word **derivations**.
- If any are false, find out the true derivations and write them down.
- Add an interesting word derivation of your own to the chart.

Word	Derivation	True or false?
noon	This is derived from the Latin word for 'ninth'. In ancient Rome the ninth hour after sunrise (3:00 p.m.) was the hottest part of the day. Most Roman people took time off to eat and rest.	
robot	This word first appeared in English in 1923. It comes from a Czech word for 'forced labour' which was used by Karel Čapek, a Czech dramatist, to refer to mechanical people constructed to do menial tasks.	
coconut	Coconut comes from the Portuguese word *coco*, meaning a grinning face. Early Portuguese explorers gave the coconut this name because the three small holes on the base of a coconut's shell reminded them of a grinning face.	
chronicle	This word is derived from *khronos*, the ancient Greek word for 'disease'. Doctors in ancient Greece would record incidences of serious diseases, in order of occurrence, in a book called a *biblia khronika*.	
salary	This comes from the Latin word *sal*, meaning salt. Roman soldiers were given an allowance for buying salt, which was at that time a valued commodity. This allowance was called a *salarium*, and came into English as 'salary'.	
panic	In ancient Greece, panic was 'terror caused by the god Pan'. Pan was believed to cause irrational fear by making spooky noises or jumping out at people.	

NOW TRY THIS!

- Find out and write down the derivations of these words. What do the words have in common?

Use an etymological dictionary.

> boycott   guillotine   loganberry   nicotine
> poinsettia   saxophone   shrapnel   silhouette

Teachers' note The pupils should use an etymological dictionary or the Internet to check whether the derivations are true or false. Encourage them to find another example which they find interesting or unusual; discuss these during the plenary session.

Eliminate the errors!

STARTER

- Cut out the cards.
- Match up the cards to make words.
  Look at how the words are made up.

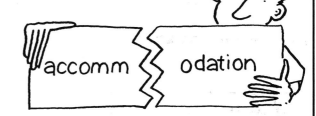

accomm ⟩ odation

Check your answers in a dictionary.

accomm ⟩	nation	con ⟩	ment
analy ⟩	ment	con ⟩	nite
argu ⟩	appoint	continu ⟩	ning
assess ⟩	cuit	defi ⟩	ment
atmo ⟩	ful	dis ⟩	sequence
beauti ⟩	ness	dis ⟩	ruary
begin ⟩	sis	desper ⟩	ous
busi ⟩	sphere	environ ⟩	odation
bis ⟩	tration	expla ⟩	ate
concen ⟩	appear	Feb ⟩	science

Teachers' note Split the class into small groups and give each group a copy of this page. When they have matched the cards, ask them to share any strategies they find useful for remembering the spellings. These might include splitting the words into root words, prefixes and suffixes (for example, *argu -ment*); splitting the words into syllables (for example, *Feb/ru/ar/y*); or finding words within words (for example, *desperate*).

Developing Literacy
Word Level
Year 9
© A & C BLACK

54

Eliminate the errors!

- In this list of commonly misspelled words, underline ten that you find difficult to spell.
- Choose a spelling strategy for each word. Write the words on the appropriate parts of the chart. Write or draw your strategies on the chart, or on another piece of paper.

fierce
fulfil
happened
height
interesting
interrupt
knowledge
marriage
miscellaneous
necessary
outrageous
permanent
persuasion
possession
preparation
prioritise
questionnaire
queue
receive
reference
remember
secondary
separate
sincerely
skilful
success
surprise
tomorrow
unfortunately
weight
weird
women

Strategy 1: Split the word into **phonemes** or **syllables**.	**Strategy 2:** Exaggerate the pronunciation of the word.
Strategy 3: Find a word within the word.	**Strategy 4:** Make up **mnemonics** such as word drawings or silly sentences.
Strategy 5: Investigate the **derivation** of root words, prefixes and suffixes.	**Strategy 6:** Use the Look, Say, Cover, Write and Check strategy.

NOW TRY THIS!

- Explain the difference in meaning between these pairs of commonly misspelled words.

| advice | affect | licence | practice |
| advise | effect | license | practise |

- Think of strategies to help you remember the difference.

Teachers' note The words provided are some of those which are most commonly misspelled. The sheet provides a resource for the pupils to record their difficulties and to think of strategies to help spell the words. Stress that everyone learns in different ways and that there is no one correct approach: whatever strategy works for the individual is valid.

New vocabulary
STARTER

Dan has written down his ideas for remembering how to spell these ICT words.

Word	Syllable structure	Spelling strategies
binary	bi/na/ry	BI means 'two'. Contains BIN. AR reminds me of PARTS. Y at the end changes the shape of the word.
connection	con/nec/tion	Double N. 'It's a con'. Remember CONNECT – gives the T in the final syllable.
delete	de/lete	LET me spell this word right! DE at the beginning – D and E also the first and last letters of the word.
interactive	in/ter/act/ive	INTER + ACTIVE = prefix + root. INTER means 'between'. Final syllable – 'I'VE got to remember the ending.'
megabyte	me/ga/byte	MEGA means 'big'. BYTE not 'bite' – think of BYE in the final syllable.

• Write your own ideas for remembering how to spell the following words.

Word	Syllable structure	Spelling strategies
cartridge		
database		
electronic		
interface		
monitor		

Teachers' note Give each pupil a copy of this page. First revise splitting words into syllables and discuss that there are different ways of doing this (for example, bi/na/ry, bin/ar/y). Model the spelling strategies with the pupils. Ask them to write their personal strategies for spelling the ICT words within a time limit of five minutes. Then invite them to share their strategies with the class.

Developing Literacy
Word Level
Year 9
© A & C BLACK

New vocabulary

- List new, difficult words you have come across in work in other subjects. Use this sheet to help you learn to spell them.

Other useful strategies are:
- *phonemes*
- *syllables*
- *shape of the word*
- *words within words*
- *exaggerated pronunciation.*

| Word | List any spelling problems at the: | | | How can derivation help? | Do spelling rules help? | Mnemonics or other strategies |
	beginning	middle	end			
alignment	only one 'l'	gn – silent 'g'	ment – unstressed 'e'	align + ment root word + suffix	Consonant suffix does not change spelling of root word.	There's no 'line' in 'alignment'!

Teachers' note This sheet encourages the pupils to look carefully at the structure and sound of words in order to highlight areas of difficulty. This will help them to find appropriate spelling strategies. They could choose a particular subject to focus on.

English subject words

STARTER

The following strategy can help you to learn new words.

Look
- Look at the length of the word.
- Look at the shape of the word.
- Notice tricky combinations of letters.
- Notice any familiar **prefixes** or **suffixes**.
- Think about whether the word belongs to a family you recognise.

Say
- Speak the word out loud.
- Sound it out **syllable** by syllable.
- Sound it out **phoneme** by phoneme.
- Spell the word letter by letter.
- Try saying the tricky parts in a particular rhythm.
- Remind yourself of the **word family**.
- Think of a rhyme or **mnemonic**.

Cover
- Cover part of the word and spell out the rest.
- Cover the whole word and say it to yourself.

Write
- Look away and write what you remember.
- Remember the shape of the word and the number of syllables it has.
- Think of the mnemonic.

Check ✓
- Look at the word again.
- Did you spell it correctly?
- If not, circle the incorrect parts.
- Think of a way of remembering them.

- Try using the strategy with these English subject words.

alliteration	apostrophe	clause
comparison	conjunction	consonant
dialogue	exclamation	imagery
metaphor	onomatopoeia	paragraph
personification	rhyme	simile

Teachers' note Photocopy this page onto an OHT. Choose one of the words from the list and model how to identify the tricky parts of the word. Then model how to apply the strategy to the word. Explain that this approach appeals to many of our senses: for example, looking at the shape of a word, hearing its sound, and remembering other words in the same family. Ask the pupils to choose other words from the list and to learn them using the strategy.

Developing Literacy
Word Level
Year 9
© A & C BLACK

English subject words

- Use this sheet to help with words you find difficult to spell in English. First list words on the appropriate notepads.

Words used in study of literature	Words used in sentence-level work	Words used in word-level work	Words used in writing

- Try out the spelling strategies below on the words. Jot down your strategy ideas on another piece of paper.
- Tick which are the most useful strategies for the different kinds of words.

Strategy	Literature	Sentence-level	Word-level	Writing
Split words into **syllables**				
Find a word within the word				
Use **mnemonics**				
Investigate the **derivation** of root words, prefixes and suffixes				
Use the Look, Say, Cover, Write and Check strategy				

Teachers' note Encourage the pupils to list the words they find difficult and to file the sheet as a personal record. Provide examples of each of the strategies on the chart (see page 60). Stress that each pupil will have his or her personal preferences for strategies, and what works for one pupil may not work for another.

Maths words

STARTER

- Cut out the cards. Choose three cards each.
- Circle the parts of the words that are difficult to spell. Then work out strategies for learning to spell the words. You could try these methods.

Split the word into **phonemes**: *c/u/b/oi/d* or **syllables**: *ra/di/us*	Find a word within the word: *fr (act) ion*	Make up **mnemonics**: *Peter runs around the perimeter.* 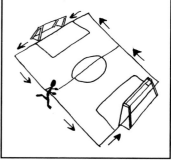
Investigate the **derivation** of root words, prefixes and suffixes: *kilo- gram*	Use the Look, Say, Cover, Write and Check strategy.	

adjacent	alternate	amount
approximately	average	calculation
centimetre	circumference	decimal
denominator	division	equilateral
horizontal	isosceles	kilometre
measure	multiplication	parallelogram

Teachers' note Split the class into groups of five pupils and give each group a copy of this page. Before beginning, talk through each of the strategies outlined to show how they can help. Encourage the pupils to share their strategies with the group, and to find other 'difficult' words that will reinforce the strategies (for example, *millilitre* and *millimetre* follow the same pattern). All the pupils will have something worthwhile to bring to this activity.

Developing Literacy
Word Level
Year 9
© A & C BLACK

Maths words

• List maths words that you find difficult to spell.

• Complete the charts to help you remember how to spell the words.

Strategy 1

• Investigate the **derivation** of the words.

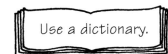

Use a dictionary.

• List other words with similar derivations.

Word	Notes on derivation	Related words
quadrilateral	quad – derived from Latin. Means 'four'. lateral – derived from Latin. Means 'side'.	quadruple equilateral

Strategy 2

• Look for a word within the word.

alternate

Word	Words inside
alternate	alter, ate, tern

Word	Words inside

Teachers' note The pupils can use this sheet as a spelling log to record words they find difficult. They could file several copies of the sheet and add to them throughout the year. Explain that the strategies may be useful for only some of the words; the pupils will need to decide which strategy works best for each word. See also page 63.

Sticky subject words
STARTER

- Cut out the cards. Pick out all the words you would use in science.

- Look up any words whose meaning you do not know.

- On the blank cards, write other science words that you find difficult to spell.

Use a dictionary.

acid	theatrical	organism
condensation	muscular	alkaline
estuary	element	pollution
evaporation	medieval	friction
vertebrate	laboratory	poverty
combustion	mammal	solution
chemical	longitude	nutrient
oxygen	settlement	particles
pressure	reproduction	temperature
solution	atlas	digestion
thermometer	photosynthesis	metaphor
erosion	respiration	apparatus

Teachers' note Split the class into small groups and give each group a copy of this page. Encourage the pupils to write definitions of words whose meanings they do not know (this could be done within a time limit of three minutes). At the end of the session, discuss the meanings of the science words and what parts of the words make them difficult to spell. Invite the pupils to share the other science words they have listed. These words can then be used with the consolidation activity.

Developing Literacy
Word Level
Year 9
© A & C BLACK

62

Sticky subject words

Subject: _____

• List words in this subject that you find difficult to spell.

• Complete the charts to help you remember how to spell the words.

Strategy 1

• Split the words into **syllables**. Practise saying the words, pronouncing each part clearly.

respiration

Word	Syllable 1	Syllable 2	Syllable 3	Syllable 4	Syllable 5
respiration	res	pi	ra	tion	

Strategy 2

• Make up **mnemonics** to help you spell the tricky parts of the words.

Word	Mnemonic
vertebrates	Many _ver_tebrates can stand _vert_ically.

Strategy 3

• Use the Look, Say, Cover, Write and Check strategy.

Teachers' note The pupils could file several copies of this sheet and add to them throughout the year. Explain that some strategies may be useful for only some of the words; the pupils will need to decide which strategy works best for each word. Discuss that there are different ways of splitting words into syllables (for example, *res/pi/ra/tion, re/spir/a/tion*). See also page 61.

Developing Literacy
Word Level
Year 9
© A & C BLACK   **63**

Glossary

adjective A word that describes a noun: for example, *blue, round, tall*.

adverb A word that gives information about a verb. It says how something happens: for example, *she shouted loudly*.

antonym prefix A prefix that can be added to a word to form a word with the opposite meaning: for example, *un- (un- + tie = untie); mis- (mis- + behave = misbehave)*.

comparative The form of an adjective or adverb used when comparing: for example, *my bag is smaller than yours; she walked more slowly than usual*.

consonant suffix A suffix that begins with a consonant: for example, *-ly, -ment, -ful, -s*.

cvc word A word made up of three letters in the order consonant–vowel–consonant: for example, *cap, hut*.

derivation Where a word comes from and its original meaning: for example, *chef* comes from the French word meaning 'head' or 'chief'; *geology* comes from the ancient Greek words *geo*, meaning 'earth', and *logos*, meaning 'word'.

homographs Words spelled the same way which are pronounced differently and have different meanings: for example, *Bow before the man with the bow tie*.

homonyms Words spelled the same way which have the same pronunciation but different meanings: for example, *We wave at the children as a wave rolls in*.

homophones Words that sound the same as one another, but are spelled differently and have different meanings: for example, *poor, pour, paw*.

long vowel sound A vowel sound that 'says its name in the alphabet': for example, *ai* in *pain*, *o* in *cone* and *y* in *sky*.

mnemonic A personal way of remembering something: for example, *There's just ice in justice*.

morphology The study of how words are formed: for example, by adding prefixes and suffixes to root words.

noun A word that names a person, place or thing: for example, *a river, the Thames*.

phoneme The smallest unit of sound in a word. It is not necessarily a syllable and can be made up of one to four letters: for example, *dog* has the phonemes *d/o/g*; *though* has the phonemes *th/ough*.

positive The usual form of an adjective or adverb (also known as the absolute form): for example, *my bag is small; she walked slowly*.

prefix A group of letters attached to the beginning of a word which change the word's meaning: for example, *dis- (dis- + approve = disapprove); re- (re- + gain = regain)*. The word does not change spelling when a prefix is added.

root word A word to which prefixes and suffixes may be added: for example, *appear (dis- + appear + -ance = disappearance); take (re- + take + -ing = retaking)*.

short vowel sound A vowel sound such as *a* in *pan*, *o* in *hot* and *u* in *up*.

silent letter A letter in a word that is not pronounced: for example, *b* in *climb*, *w* in *write* and *l* in *palm*.

suffix A group of letters attached to the end of a word which change the word's meaning and/or function: for example, *-ed (appear + -ed = appeared); -er (big + -er = bigger)*. The word may change spelling when a suffix is added.

superlative The form of an adjective or adverb used to express the highest degree of a quality: for example, *my bag is the smallest; she walked the most slowly of all*.

syllable A rhythmic sound unit of a word. Each syllable should contain at least one vowel or a *y*: for example, *al/though* has two syllables; *syl/lab/le* has three.

unstressed vowel A vowel that is difficult to make out when spoken because it is uttered quickly or quietly: for example, *a* in *extraordinary*.

verb A word or group of words indicating action or a state of being: for example, *is, grow, reached*.

vowel phoneme A phoneme that makes a vowel sound: for example, *o* in *dog*, *ough* in *though*, *ea* in *lean* and *y* in *sky*.

vowel suffix A suffix that begins with a vowel or *y*: for example, *-ed, -ing, -able, -y*.

word family A group of words derived from the same root word: for example, *assign, design, resign, signal, signature* and *significant* (all from the root word *sign* and belonging to the same word family).

word root The part of a word that remains when all prefixes and suffixes are removed: for example, *sol* (Latin for 'sun') is the word root of *solar* and *parasol*.

Developing Literacy: Word Level Year 9 © A & C BLACK